HANUMAN'S
BIG GIG

by
Swamini Supriyananda

Chinmaya Mission UK
2 Egerton Gardens
London NW4 4BA
www.chinmayauk.org
www.chinmayabooks.com
Find us on Amazon
info@chinmayauk.org
Tel: 0208 203 6288
UK registered charity 1077622

C·H·I·N·M·A·Y·A B·A·L·A K·A·T·H·A

Hanuman loves Shri Ram,
with all his heart and soul.
So Hanuman loves anything
and everything to do with Ram.

Hanuman loves to listen
to stories about Ram.
He loves to sing Ram's name.
He loves to serve Ram
in any way and everyway.

But no one can hear Hanuman or see him!
Hanuman has magic.

There is someone else who loves God a lot... Narada Muni. Even he likes to sing God's name. Even he has magic.

One day, as Naradji was singing, everyone started praising him.

"Oh, Naradji, you have such a sweet voice!"
said the first person.

"You play the *veena* so well,"
said the second person.

"You are by far the best musician I have heard,"
said a third person.

Naradji simply smiled at them, and left.

Narad Muni began thinking "People are saying I sing very well, I must be good, maybe even very good."

Oh no! Oh dear! Instead of thinking of God, Narad Muni started thinking "I sing so well!"

He started singing wherever and whenever he had a crowd to listen to him, because he wanted to hear them praise him.

Oh no! Oh dear! He started showing off.

Narada Muni even started showing off to Krishna.
Krishna waited and watched but Naradji just would not stop.
Krishna is very clever and can see into everyone's heart.
Krishna saw into Naradji's heart and there was no love.

"Oh no! Oh, dear!" said Krishna to Himself,
"Naradji has become proud, and when pride creeps into
   a devotee's heart, it takes him away from the Lord.
   I must do something to help him."

With a twinkle in His eye, Krishna said,
"Naradji, will you come and play
your *veena* at my party?"

Naradji was so happy!
Now even Krishna was praising him!

Naradji did love Krishna!
In fact he loved Krishna very much.
But he was starting to forget
how much he loved Krishna,
because he was too busy showing off.

At Krishna's beautiful party there were dancers and singers, artists and sculptors, saints and sages.

There was also a very special guest,
super super special indeed – Hanuman!
Shhhh... No-one knew or recognized him.

Krishna had a mischievous smile and
a naughty twinkle in His eye.

It was time for Naradji to sing.
He cleared his throat...ah..hmm, he stood up taller,
and with great show he put his hands on his *veena*.

Everyone listened as the music filled the hall.
Everyone clapped and cheered:
"Wonderful!", "Superb!"

Krishna asked Hanuman,
"Oh, Monkey Chief,
what did you think of
Naradji's singing?"

Naradji was a little irritated
and thought to himself,
"Why is He asking a monkey
about my singing?
What would a monkey know
about music?"

Krishna knows what we are thinking, and
Krishna knows what we are feeling, so Krishna said,
"Naradji, you might be surprised how much
this monkey knows about singing.
Why don't you lend him your *veena*
and let him sing?"

Naradji got angrier and this time said aloud, "My *veena* is a very delicate instrument, and I really like my *veena*! I am not going to give it to a monkey! He will only break it!"

Krishna smiled His special smile again, and said,
"Don't worry, my dear Narad, your *veena* will be fine.
You can hold Me responsible for it."

Naradji did love Krishna, and trusted Him,
so he handed his *veena* over to the Monkey Chief.

Krishna then looked at
Hanuman and said,
"Now, let us hear
your charming music."

Hanumanji took the *veena* and rested it on the stone
in front of him. He closed his eyes, dived deep into his heart
and remembered Shri Ram. His heart overflowed with love,
and he started to sing,
"Shri Ram, Jai Ram, Jai Jai Ram...
  Shri Ram, Jai Ram, Jai Jai Ram."

Everyone became still, their eyes fixed on Hanuman.
Everyone became so peaceful listening to him sing,
and their hearts were filled with love and joy.
Hanuman's love for Ram melted everyone's heart.
It even melted the stone in front of him!

When Hanumanji finished, everyone sat in silence, wonderstruck for a few moments. Then they started praising him even more than they had praised Naradji. Even Naradji praised him.

Krishna said, "Naradji, it is good that you, too, see his talents and can praise him."

Naradji hung his head in shame. He said, "I am sorry for thinking badly of him. You are the Lord. You know everyone's heart."

Then Naradji tried to take back his *veena*.
But it would not move. It was stuck!

"What kind of trick is this?!," said Naradji.
"I cannot lift my *veena*.
Give me back my precious *veena*!"

"Ok, wait, wait," said Krishna.
"Let the others help you lift it."

Many strong men
came forward
but the *veena*
would not move.

An old musician said, "I noticed the stone on which the *veena* was placed melted when the Monkey Chief sang, and thus sank a little. When the music stopped, it hardened again and the *veena* got stuck in it."

"Oh, then the solution is simple," said Krishna, before turning to Narada Muni.

"Naradji, why don't you sing so that the stone melts again, then you can take your *veena* back?" said Krishna, with a cheeky twinkle in His eyes.

So Naradji sang... and sang...
sang the very best he could...
but the stone would not melt!

Tired and embarrassed, he stopped singing
and hung his head in shame.

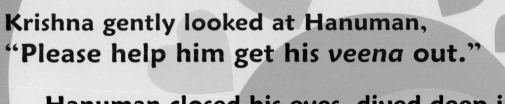

Krishna gently looked at Hanuman,
"Please help him get his *veena* out."

Hanuman closed his eyes, dived deep into his heart and
remembered Shri Ram. His heart overflowed with love,
and he started to sing,
"Shri Ram, Jai Ram, Jai Jai Ram...
Shri Ram, Jai Ram, Jai Jai Ram."

Soon enough, the stone started melting, and Naradji quickly retrieved his *veena*.

When Naradji looked up at Krishna, the Lord smiled His special smile. In that moment, in a flash, Naradji knew that Krishna was taking away his pride, so that he would never ever show off again.

Naradji bowed deeply to Krishna. He loved Krishna.
He remembered in his heart that he loved Krishna
more than being good at playing the *veena*.
He had just forgotten for a while,
and he was so glad Shri Krishna reminded him.

Pride takes us away from the Lord,
while humility brings us closer to Him.

Narada Muni forgot about people's praises, and singing better than others. He remembered Krishna's kind and loving smile, and sang for Krishna. Naradji was much happier, and his music sounded much sweeter.

Shhhhh! Don't tell him.

Lucky Krishna can see into our hearts, and knows how to take the yucky bits away.

Hanuman loves Ram, and he really loves to sing Ram's name.
Therefore, Hanumanji's music melted everyone's heart,
and even melted stone...

If you sing with love,
maybe...

You will melt Hanuman's heart.

Are you singing yet?
Is Hanuman's heart melting?